COLOURS

RED

Gabrielle Woolfitt

WAYLAND

First published in Great Britain in 2016 by Wayland

ISBN: 978 1 5263 0182 6

10 9 8 7 6 5 4 3 2 1

Wayland
An imprint of
Hachette Children's Group
Part of Hodder & Stoughton
Carmelite House
50 Victoria Embankment
London EC4Y 0DZ

An Hachette UK Company
www.hachette.co.uk
www.hachettechildrens.co.uk
A catalogue for this title is available from the British Library

Printed and bound in China

Produced for Wayland by
White-Thomson Publishing Ltd
www.wtpub.co.uk

Editor: Izzi Howell
Designer: Rocket Design (East Anglia) Ltd
Picture researcher: Izzi Howell
Wayland editor: Vicky Brooker

The author Gabrielle Woolfitt is a qualified teacher, specialising in science.

picture acknowledgements:
The author and publisher would like to thank the following agencies and people for allowing these pictures to be reproduced:

Alamy: Travel Pictures 15, epa european pressphoto agency b.v. 22; iStock: _maeterlinck_ 4tl, HPphoto 4cl, pepifoto 4bl, NormanKrauss 8, tap10 10l, AnaDiana 10r, Hongqi Zhang 12, pidjoe 13t, fotostorm 13c, Delpixart 20l; Shutterstock: jeka84 cover, Ewais title page, andrey_l 4tr, azure1 4cr, Michael Wick 6, Regien Paassen 7t, Martin Fowler 7b, Marco Uliana 9, Alena Ozerova 10, Wasu Watcharadachaphong 13b, Duplass 14, Africa Studio 16tr, NIPAPORN PANYACHAROEN 16bl, Alexandra Lande 16cr, ER_09 17, EpicStockMedia 18, Maryna Kulchytska 19l, Elena_Denisova 19r, PhIllStudio 20r, gornjak 21, Suzanne Tucker 23, SP-Photo 24t, Czy 24b, ImageFlow 25tl, hxdbzxy 25tr, rmnoa357 25bl, stocksolutions 25br, Stanislav Fosenbauer 26, cdrw 27t, jackapong 27c, Art_girl 27b, Dario Sabljak 28, beboy 29l, Botond Horvath 29tr, Maryna Kulchytska 31.

All design elements from Shutterstock.

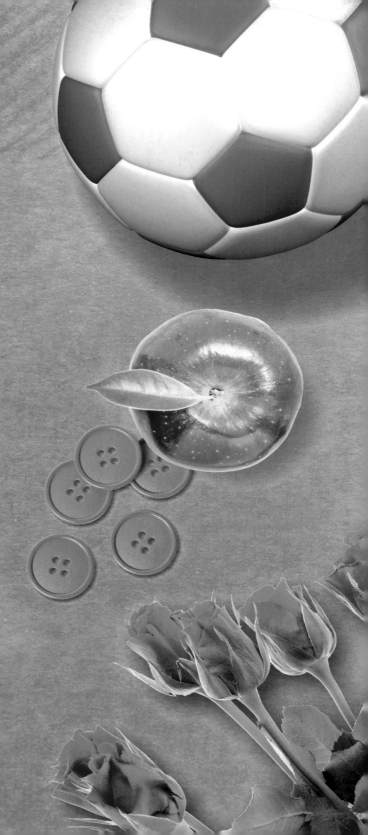

CONTENTS

WHAT IS RED?

RED IS A BEAUTIFUL COLOUR. ROSES AND RUBIES ARE RED. RED IS A NATURAL COLOUR. SUNSETS AND AUTUMN LEAVES ARE RED.

Juicy cherries are **RED**.

Red balloons are **FUN**.

Red is a strong colour. Red is a **PARTY** colour.

4

Make a red picture.
Use red pencils and pens. Splash
on some red paint. Try mixing
different shades of red together.
Cut out pictures of red things
from magazines. Stick on some
red buttons. Colour it in with red
crayons. Tie on a big red ribbon.

That's what red is!

RED ALERT

Red is a **WARNING COLOUR**. The red man signal at a pedestrian crossing means **DO NOT** cross the road.

A red flag flying on the beach means the sea is **DANGEROUS**. If you go swimming you might drown.

What does a **RED TRAFFIC LIGHT** mean?

Red is also a warning colour in nature. Fly Agaric toadstools are red and **VERY POISONOUS**. They are dangerous to eat.

Yew berries are bright red. If you ate them **YOU WOULD BECOME ILL**.

RED ANIMALS

The **FRIGATE BIRD** is usually dark and plain.

When he wants to find a mate he grows **RED FEATHERS**.

When he sees a **FEMALE** he puffs up his chest to look as **STRONG** as he can.

PEACOCK BUTTERFLIES are very brightly coloured. This means birds can see them easily. But the birds do not eat them. Their wing spots look like eyes. Birds think the butterfly is a big animal. Find out about some other red animals.

RED
PEOPLE

◀ **This girl has red hair and freckles.**

Sometimes white people go red. When they are hot, blood under the skin cools them down.

When they are angry or embarrassed, they blush. It only lasts a little while. What makes you angry?

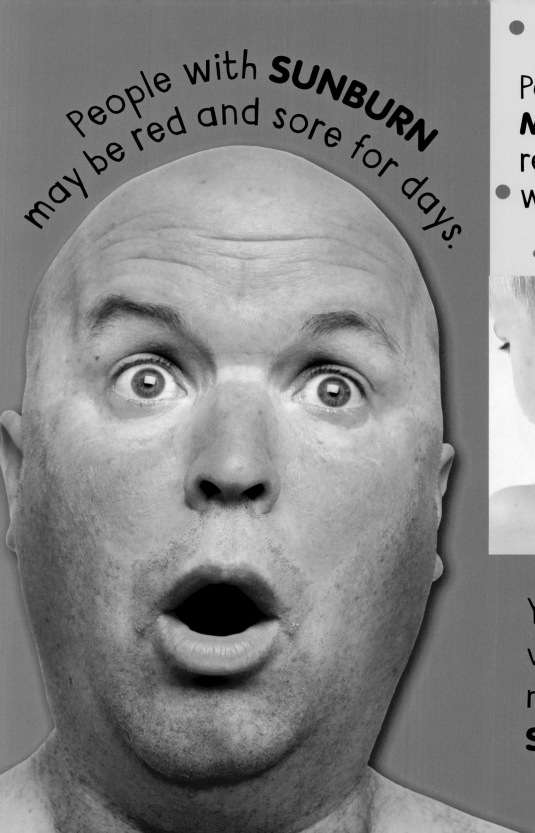

People with **SUNBURN** may be red and sore for days.

People with **MEASLES** have red spots for weeks.

You must be very careful not to get **SUNBURNT**.

RED
MAKE-UP

When do people wear make-up? Why do they wear red make-up? Here are some ideas.

LOOK AT THESE HANDS.

This Indian woman has painted them for a wedding. She has used henna. Henna is a red **PLANT DYE**.

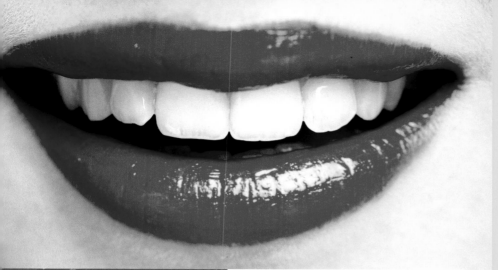

Some women use make-up to look smart. They wear **RED LIPSTICK** and **NAIL POLISH**.

This boy is wearing red face paint to look like an animal.

Red powder makes cheeks look rosy. This is called **BLUSHER**.

RED FESTIVALS

Red is a bright colour. Red is easy to see. If you wear a red outfit, **EVERYONE WILL NOTICE YOU**.

People wear red clothes for parties and **FESTIVALS**.

This girl has dressed up like **SANTA CLAUS!**

A **RED RIBBON** makes hair look smart and neat.

This red dragon is Chinese.

Red is the colour of **GOOD LUCK** in China. The dancers hope the dragon will bring them good fortune.

RED FOOD

Pomegranates are full of **tasty** seeds.

Which red foods give **RED JUICE?** You can dye material with red juice.

You can grow **RASPERRIES.**

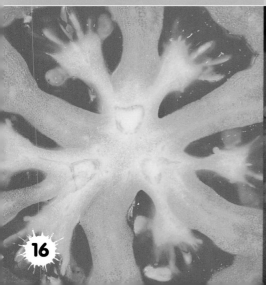

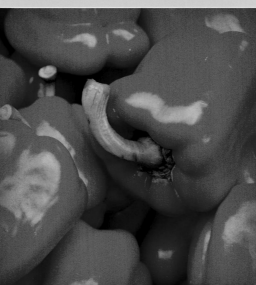

Do you like **SWEET** red fruit and **CRISP** red vegetables?

16

In the summer, **COOL DOWN** with a juicy **PIECE** of watermelon?

RED STORIES

Red sky at night,
Shepherd's delight.
Red sky in the morning,
Shepherd's warning.

Do you know what this old rhyme means?

There are red things in lots of **STORIES** and **SONGS**.

Can you make up a poem about the colour **RED**?

Here is a story about a red hen.

Once upon a time, there was a little red hen who lived on a farm. She was friends with a lazy dog, a sleepy cat, and a noisy yellow duck ...

Do you know the story of **LITTLE RED RIDING HOOD**? Or **RUDOLPH THE RED-NOSED REINDEER**?

Do **YOU** know the rest of the story?

19

Red flowers are often used as signs. Different flowers have different meanings.

RED FLOWERS

Red roses are a sign of **LOVE**.

Red holly berries are a symbol of **CHRISTMAS**. Can you think of some other red flowers?

Over one hundred years ago, there was a **TERRIBLE WAR** in Europe. Many people were killed. The battlefields they fought in were full of red poppies. So **RED POPPIES** remind us of people who died in wars.

THE RED CROSS

When you hurt yourself you need **FIRST AID**.

The Red Cross helps people who get hurt in wars all over the world.

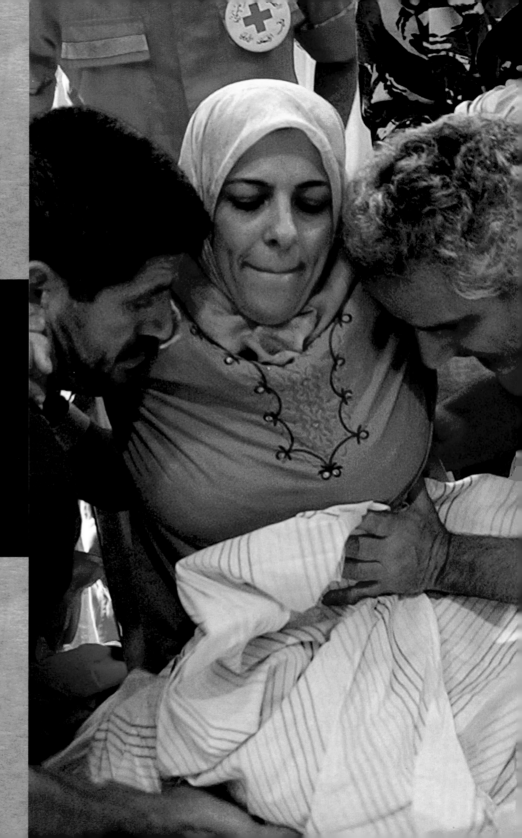

This boy fell over. Now he has a **RED GRAZE** on his elbow.

TO HELP HIM:
Clean and dry the graze and put a plaster on it.

If somebody is badly hurt they need a **DOCTOR**.

Do you know how to find your doctor's phone number? Learn how to phone for an ambulance.

RED SHAPES

We can see red shapes every day. Traffic lights are red **CIRCLES**. Where else do you see red shapes?

What shape is a clown's **NOSE?**

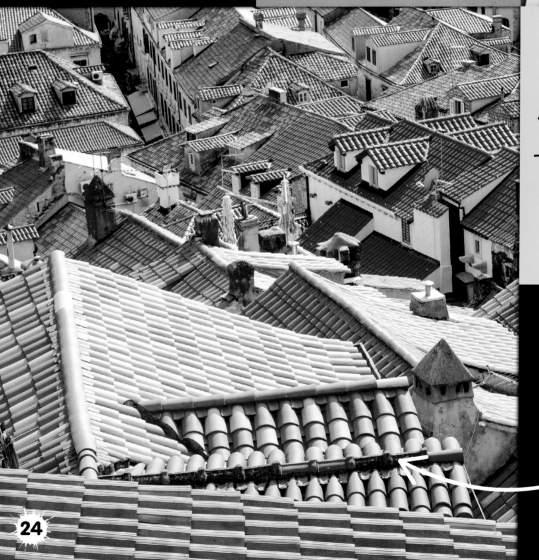

Sometimes roof tiles are red, too. How many different red shapes can you count?

WHAT SHAPE ARE FLAGS?

These flags have red shapes on them. Can you say what each shape is? You will find a **STAR**, a **CROSS**, a **MAPLE LEAF** and a **CIRCLE**.

RED IN NATURE

This huge red rock is called Uluru. It is in the middle of the **DESERT** in Australia.

Some things in nature turn red. It is autumn when the leaves turn red and forests look beautiful.

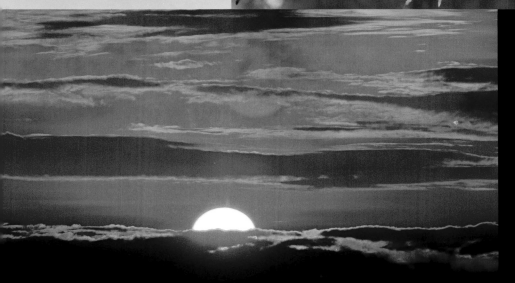

Sometimes the sky looks red when the sun sets.

Some things in nature are always red. **RUBIES** are beautiful red stones, found in the ground.

Rubies are **TRANSPARENT** and sparkly. They are used to make jewellery.

RED-HOT

Things that are red-hot are often beautiful but dangerous. This red-hot cooker ring could burn you.

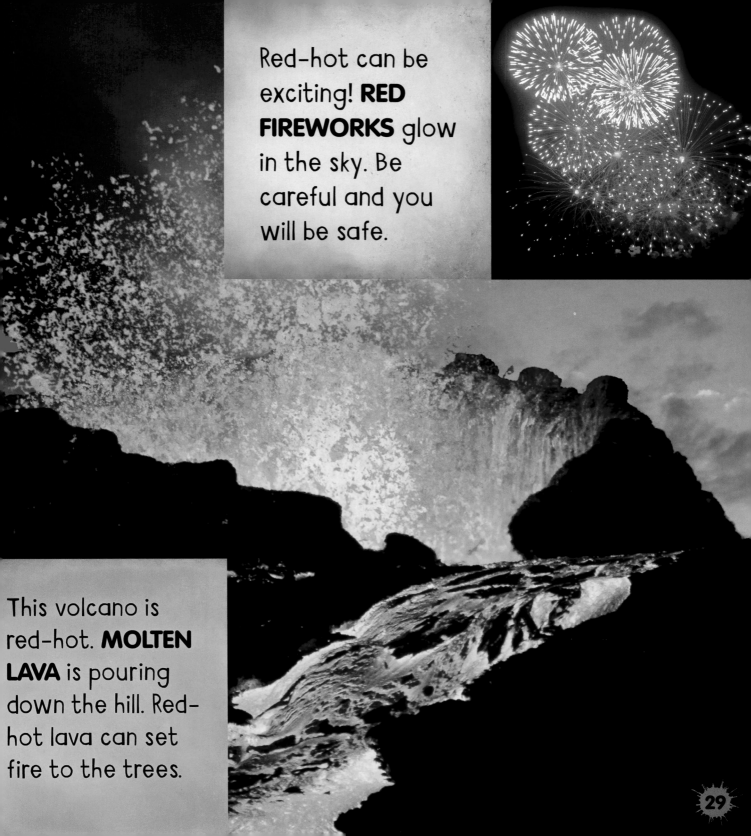

Red-hot can be exciting! **RED FIREWORKS** glow in the sky. Be careful and you will be safe.

This volcano is red-hot. **MOLTEN LAVA** is pouring down the hill. Red-hot lava can set fire to the trees.

MAKE IT YOURSELF

Please ask an adult to help you with these projects.

1 SAFETY PROJECT

Look around your home and school. Where is it dangerous?
Which places get hot? Where could you cut yourself?

Make some **RED ALERT** signs to warn people of the danger.
Make a **FIRST AID BOX** in case of accidents.

Ouch Alert!
Table has
sharp edge

Caution
Cooker may
be hot!

Red Alert
These
knives are
dangerous

Here are some
signs, can you think
of some more?

2 RED PARTY

Plan a red party. Ask all the guests to wear **RED CLOTHES**. They could use red make-up or face paints. You could put **HENNA** on your hands!

Write a list of friends to invite to the party. Make **INVITATION CARDS** to give to your friends.

Make a red meal. You could serve:
- ★ tomato salad ★ sausages
- ★ red pepper pizza ★ cherryade
- ★ strawberry jelly ★ red plums
- ★ raspberry ripple ice cream

Decorate the room with **RED BALLOONS** and **STREAMERS**. Have a cake with **RED ICING** and candles. Make up some **RED SONGS**. Don't forget a red going home present.

Have a great time!

Wow, that's a super red party dress!

GLOSSARY

Ambulance   A special van that takes people to hospital.

Blush   To go red in the face and feel hot.

Desert   A sandy or stony place where there is very little rain.

Dye   A liquid that is used to change the colour of clothes, skin and hair.

Festival   A celebration with special food and music.

First aid   Emergency help given to someone who is hurt in an accident.

Lava   The hot liquid rock from a volcano.

Mate   The male or female of a pair of animals.

Molten   Made into liquid by heat.

Rhyme   A poem with words that sound alike at the ends of the lines.

Symbol   Something that stands for or means something else.

Transparent   See-through.

Volcano   A mountain that sometimes erupts and molten lava comes out.

INDEX